MY DREAMS & GOALS

JOURNAL

Terri Savelle Foy

WITH BONUS "5 YEARS FROM NOW" SECTION

You are a part of a special group of people. Everyone has a dream they would like to accomplish, but only a relative few will actually do the work needed to see it happen. Just by the fact you are reading this now, means you are serious about moving forward and going after your dreams.

Today is the perfect time for you to begin planning and setting goals for your life.

Do you know about the African impala? They can jump almost 10 feet high and 30 feet long. Yet, you can find them in a zoo behind a 4 foot wall. Why? The impala will not attempt to jump to where it can't see first. Since it can't see over the four foot wall, it just stays confined year after year in that small area.

God doesn't want you confined to the life you've been living or perhaps the life you've settled for. He wants you to dream, to set goals, to see beyond where you are to where He wants to take you. You have to see where you're headed before you start taking steps.

The Bible tells us in Proverbs 29:18, "Where there is no vision, the people perish." I looked up the word perish and it means die! You are dying inside when you have no vision.

What do you want? Don't just live life from day to day, doing your routine, never setting goals and reaching for something more.

How much do you want to give to a charity or your favorite ministry next year? What's the amount? Write it down. Set a goal. Stretch yourself. What do you see?

The first step to achieving your dreams is that you have to see it. Picture your dreams. You've got to see something before you can build something.

If you don't have a picture in your mind and heart of what you want to do with your life, then you're just busy. You're just killing time. That is not God's best for your life.

Most people do not invest time into using one of the most wonderful gifts God has given us. Our imagination. Everything gets its start in the imagination. Have you stopped using your imagination? Have you stopped seeing beyond your present circumstances?

Once you give yourself permission to dream, you will begin recognizing God-given opportunities all around you that you never noticed before. At the moment you become conscious of your ultimate dreams and desires in life, your spirit will go to work to bring those dreams to pass.

Albert Einstein said, "Your imagination is a preview of life's coming attractions." The problem is that many people never allow themselves to imagine or dream about the possibilities God may have for them. God wants to show you what He sees. He sees the end from the beginning. He sees the big picture. He wants you to see it too. It requires spending some time with Him in prayer and just asking Him, "Lord, what do you want me to do?" And then listen. Dream. Write. Think. Imagine."

Your dream could be to build a dream house. See it inside. Imagine it. Build an image of that dream on the inside of you and then get it on paper. Your dream could be to get your house in order. Maybe it's all cluttered right now and you've just gotten used to living that way. Get a picture of it organized and everything in its place. Put that dream on paper.

Your dream could be to go back to school and get your degree. See a degree with your name on it: "Bachelor of Arts degree --- your name". Your dream could be to lose weight and live healthy. Get a picture of it. What is your ideal weight? Write it down. Keep it in front of you. You've got to picture yourself in your dreams.

Let's make something clear. There aren't any special powers from the universe that make this work. It is simply a tool to help you get organized, focus going after your God-given dreams, and exercise your faith.

Your imagination—picturing what you want—acts as a GPS system. Once you begin to SEE YOURSELF doing what you want to do, your mind begins to head in that direction. It's like you've finally given yourself a destination to enter and now, you can begin driving. Rather than just sitting there in NEUTRAL for another year you can begin driving toward your goal!

God said to Abraham in Genesis 13, "Lift up now your eyes and look from the place where you are…" In other words, get a vision of where you want to be. In Jeremiah 1:11, we see the Lord ask, "Jeremiah, what do you see?" Ask yourself today, "What do you see? What do you see yourself doing? What do you see God doing in your life?"

When what you see inside becomes more real than what you see outside, it's just a matter of time before God will bring ideas, opportunities, resources and relationships for you to pursue those dreams.

The time to plan is now so that next year at this time, you can look back and say, "Wow! I am not the person I used to be! Look what God did in my life in one year's time because I had a plan!" It's time to get moving and pursue your dreams. Stop looking at where you are and start looking at where you want to be.

It's been said that goals that are not written down are just wishes. Don't come to the end of your life only wishing you had done more during your time on Earth. Have the confidence that you did exactly what God was counting on you to do. How do you get started? Simply grab a pen and some paper.

What I am experiencing in my own life and in this ministry is all a part of the vision and dreams God's given me that I have actually written down.

This teaching comes straight from the Bible. Habakkuk 2:2 (The Message) says, "And then God answered: 'Write this. Write what you see. Write it out in big block letters so that it can be read on the run. The vision-message is a witness pointing to what's coming. It aches for the coming – it can hardly wait! And it doesn't lie. If it seems slow in coming, wait. It's on its way. It will come right on time."

There was a man who was featured in a national magazine article because he made a list of all the things he wanted to do before he died. He had been inspired to do this by his grandmother who would constantly say, "I wish I had done that when I was younger." This man decided that he would never say that when he got older.

He was 15 years old when he wrote a list which included 127 tasks. By the end of his life, he had accomplished 108 of the 127 things he set out to do! Many of us have not accomplished one thing we wanted to do. Many of us haven't even gotten started by making such a list! Can you see the importance of writing down goals and visions on paper? Those who write their goals accomplish significantly more than those who do not.

If you're going through a painful time in your life, you especially need goals surrounding you in every area of life. If you're going to get through the storm, you have to incorporate goal planning and executing that plan in your daily routine.

Virginia Tech professor, Dave Kohl, discovered through research that 80% of Americans claim to have no goals for life; 16% have goals but are not in writing; less than 4% write down their goals but only 1% review them on a consistent basis. The 1% were all millionaires.

Napoleon Hill said, "I can teach anybody how to get what they truly want in life. The problem is I can't find anybody who can tell me what they truly want." Do you really know what you want? Do you have a clear, compelling vision in front of you that motivates you to get up each morning? Most people do not. Most, unfortunately, are just existing year after year with no purpose in life. Don't repeat this year what you did last year.

The question is: what are your dreams and goals for life?

THINK about what you want to do with the rest of your life.

- Where do you want to go?
- What do you want to see?
- Who do you want to meet?
- What do you want to achieve?
- How much money do you want to have?
- How do you want to be remembered?
- What do you want to be remembered for?

Is it written down? There is power in writing your dreams and goals.

Writing down a list of goals is a habit that successful people live by. Having a plan is what gets your eyes off the past and into the present and future. Cosmetic genius Mary Kay Ash is the founder of a beauty line that has reached $2.4 billion in wholesale sales in the United States alone. She attributed her success to the fact that every day she wrote down the six most important things to do that day.

There is a saying that the secret of your future is hidden in your daily routine. Changes need to be made on a regular basis in order to experience freedom from the past and to lead you towards your dreams and goals. Nothing happens overnight. You have to prepare for a successful future. You have to formulate a plan. You have to put it into action. Only then will you walk into a future that is full of purpose.

Here are some guidelines to remember as you think about your own goals:
1.) Goals must be in writing. "Thinking you can keep your goals in your head is just an excuse for not writing them down." (Remember Habakkuk 2:2)

2.) Goals must be measurable. There's a big difference in saying, "I want to lose weight" and saying "I will lose 10 pounds by July 1." or "I will spend 20 minutes a day walking." Your goals must be measured by something; this is what increases your chances of achieving them.

3.) Goals must be realistic. If your goals are completely unrealistic, then you're setting yourself up for defeat. If your goal is to get closer to God, then you need to be realistic in how you plan to get closer to God. Don't tell yourself you will pray for four hours every day. Be practical and set aside 10 minutes of alone time a day. It's important to set realistic and attainable goals so that you are able to reach them.

4.) Goals must have a deadline. Isn't it amazing how a deadline causes us to work harder? When my sister and I were younger, and we were told to unload the dishwasher, we would look at the clock and see if we could get it done in less than four minutes. We were determined to reach our goal. Why? We had a deadline. Always assign a deadline to your goals. It's energizing and motivating.

This journal was created to help you create and accomplish your goals and dreams. I recommend you set goals in the six key areas in life that I set goals in: Faith, Family/Household, Finances, Fitness, Friendships, and Future Dreams.

It's also important to sow toward your dreams and goals. Every time you write something down that you want to achieve or do, your next step should be to give. The Bible teaches us that a person's harvest in life depends entirely on what he or she sows.

In the book of Genesis, God gave man two things: authority and seed. Jerry Savelle says that God was teaching man that he could determine his own destiny and his own success by the seeds he sows. The seed that you sow may not always be money. You can also sow your time, talents, kindness, etc. Remember this though, you may not have what you need to fulfill your dreams, but you are never without the seed that will produce them. On each page, you are given a space to document, record and keep track of the seeds you're sowing towards your goals.

Genesis 8:22 says, "As long as the earth remains, seedtime and harvest, cold and heat, summer and winter, day and night will never cease." Make an investment in your dreams.

As you decide your habits, your habits will decide your future. When you make a habit of focusing on the things you want to accomplish and spend your energy on things that will build up your faith and your emotional, physical, and mental wellbeing, it will lead you straight into God's perfect plan for your life.

Why? Because the secret of your future is hidden in your daily routine. It's what you do every single day that matters. Don't just think in terms of goals; think habits! You can do it; you just need to get started.

And finally, Romans 4:17 says, "We serve a God who gives life to the dead and speaks of nonexistent things as if they (already) existed."

It's not enough just to imagine it and write it, you've got to speak it. Some things will never happen in your life until you begin speaking them out loud. Why? You believe yourself more than anyone and what you repeatedly hear, you will eventually believe. Take a couple of minutes every day to declare your goals fulfilled. Thank God and the more you believe it, the more you'll experience it.

Invest the time it takes to plan your life. Think about what God wants you to do, to have, to give. Listen for His voice. Listen for those God-inspired ideas. Write them down.

Remember, Proverbs 29:18 says, "Where there is no vision, the people perish (die)!" When Helen Keller was asked, "What could be worse than having no sight?" She replied, "To have sight, but have no vision."
Write your vision. Make it plain. Run right to it.

"You don't have to be great to get started, but you do have to get started to be great."
- Lee J. Co

SCRIPTURES TO CONFESS:

I do not fret or have any anxiety about anything; but in every circumstance and in everything by prayer and petition (definite requests), with thanksgiving, I make my wants known to God.
- Philippians 4:6

I remember the Lord my God, for it is He who gives me the ability to produce wealth, and so confirms His covenant, which He swore to my forefather.
- Deuteronomy 8:18

The Lord shall command the blessing upon me in my storehouse and in all that I undertake. The Lord makes me to have a surplus of prosperity through the fruit of my body. He blesses me in the land which He gives me.
- Deuteronomy 28:8-11

Everything I do will prosper.
- Psalm 1:3

Because I seek (inquire of and require) the Lord (by right of my need and on the authority of His Word), I shall not lack any beneficial thing.
- Psalm 34:10

I give and (gifts) are given to me; good measure, pressed down, shaken together and running over. For with the measure I deal out (with the measure I use when I confer benefits on others) it will be measured back to me.
- Luke 6:38

I keep out of debt and owe nobody anything except love.
- Romans 13:8

If I sow sparingly and grudgingly, I will also reap sparingly and grudgingly, and if I sow generously (that blessings may come to someone) I will also reap generously and with blessings. I give as I have made up my own mind and purposed in my heart, not reluctantly or sorrowfully or under compulsion, for God loves (He takes pleasure in, prizes above other things, and is unwilling to abandon or to do without) a cheerful (joyous, prompt to do it) giver (whose heart is in his giving).
- 2 Corinthians 9:6–7

My God will meet all my needs according to His glorious riches in Christ Jesus.
- Philippians 4:19

God wants me to prosper and be in health even as my soul prospers.
- 3 John 2

INSPIRATIONAL QUOTES

Today's preparation determines tomorrow's achievement.
- Author Unknown

The best thing in every noble dream is the dreamer...
- Moncure Conway

Dreams are the touchstones of our character.
- Henry David Thoreau

The purpose of life is a life of purpose.
- Robert Byrne

Nothing happens unless first we dream.
- Carl Sandburg

An intelligent plan is the first step to success. The man who plans knows where he is going, knows what progress he is making and has a pretty good idea when he will arrive. Planning is the open road to your destination.
- Basil S. Walsh

Without leaps of imagination, or dreaming, we lose the excitement of possibilities. Dreaming, after all, is a form of planning.
- Gloria Steinem

People are never more insecure than when they become obsessed with their fears at the expense of their dreams.
- Norman Cousins

A man's dreams are an index to his greatness.
- Zadok Rabinowitz

Unless you have definite, precise, clearly set goals, you are not going to realize the maximum potential that lies within you.
- Zig Ziglar

Dream no small dreams for they have no power to move the hearts of men.
- Johann Wolfgang von Goethe

Twenty years from now you will be more disappointed by the things that you didnít do than by the ones you did do. So throw off the bowlines. Sail away from the safe harbor. Catch the trade winds in your sails. Explore. Dream. Discover.
- Mark Twain

Goals are not only absolutely necessary to motivate us. They are essential to really keep us alive.
- Robert H. Schuller

You are never too old to set another goal or to dream a new dream.
- C.S. Lewis

Give me a stock clerk with a goal and Iíll give you a man who will make history. Give me a man with no goals and Iíll give you a stock clerk.
- J.C. Penney

FAITH SCRIPTURES & QUOTES

Fear ends where faith begins.
- Author Unknown

And without faith it is impossible to please God, because anyone who comes to him must believe that he exists and that he rewards those who earnestly seek him.
- Hebrews 11:1

Faith is daring the soul to go beyond what the eyes can see.
- William Newton Clark

Anything God asks us to do He supplies us with the energy and grace to do it.
- Author Unknown

But seek first his kingdom and his righteousness, and all these things will be given to you as well.
- Matthew 6:33

When God calls you to do something, He enables you to do it.
- Robert Schuller

Do not conform any longer to the pattern of this world, but be transformed by the renewing of your mind. Then you will be able to test and approve what God's will is, his good, pleasing and perfect will.
- Romans 12:2

Goal: I weigh my perfect weight of 155 lbs **Date Goal Set:** February 1st

Monthly progress toward the goal:		**Update:**
1st Day Of:	January	
1st Day Of:	February	Weighed in at 190 lbs
1st Day Of:	March	Down a full pants size!
1st Day Of:	April	Lost 9 lbs
1st Day Of:	May	Weighed in at 165
1st Day Of:	June	Lost 8 lbs
1st Day Of:	July	Down another dress size
1st Day Of:	August	Lost 4 lbs
1st Day Of:	September	Fit into my wedding dress again!
1st Day Of:	October	Weighed in at 150 lbs!!!
1st Day Of:	November	
1st Day Of:	December	

Date goal achieved: October 1st

☑ **GOAL ACHIEVED**

Scriptures I declare for this goal:

Phil 4:13 - I can do all things through Christ who strengthens me.

I Cor 6:19-20 - My body is the temple of the Holy Spirit and I will glorify God in my body.

Seed I sow for this goal:

$100 to my Mom

Goal: Save $5,000 this year **Date Goal Set:** January 7th

Monthly progress toward the goal:		Update:
1st Day Of:	January	Set up auto deposit into my savings account
1st Day Of:	February	$500 in savings
1st Day Of:	March	Mom gave me $100 I put it in my savings
1st Day Of:	April	Sold my old bed for $500!
1st Day Of:	May	$1,800 in savings!
1st Day Of:	June	Put $500 plus an extra $300 in savings
1st Day Of:	July	$3,100 in savings
1st Day Of:	August	Got a raise and put $300 in savings
1st Day Of:	September	$3,900 in savings
1st Day Of:	October	Garage sale gave me $250 for savings
1st Day Of:	November	$4,700 in savings
1st Day Of:	December	wohooo! $5,125 in savings!

Date goal achieved: December 29th

☑ **GOAL ACHIEVED**

Scriptures I declare for this goal:

Deuteronomy 8:18 - Lord, you have given me the ability to get wealth

Philippians 4:19 - My God supplies all my needs

Proverbs 21:20 - I am wise and have wealthy and luxury

Seed I sow for this goal:

$300 into my Church building program

Goal: I write and publish my book **Date Goal Set:** January 12th

Monthly progress toward the goal: **Update:**

1st Day Of:	January	Finished my book outline
1st Day Of:	February	talked to a self-publishing coach
1st Day Of:	March	Finished chapter 3
1st Day Of:	April	Researched print-on demand companies
1st Day Of:	May	Hired a cover designer
1st Day Of:	June	Finished the rough draft!!!
1st Day Of:	July	Sent manuscript to editor
1st Day Of:	August	Hired a designer to layout the book!
1st Day Of:	September	Approved final cover design and layout
1st Day Of:	October	Ordered ISBN #
1st Day Of:	November	PUBLISHED MY BOOK!!
1st Day Of:	December	

Date goal achieved: November 9th

☑ **GOAL ACHIEVED**

Scriptures I declare for this goal:

Jeremiah 30:2 - Write all the words which I have spoken to you in a book.

Psalm 37:4 - He will give me the desires of my heart.

Seed I sow for this goal:

$200 to my favorite author

Goal: ______________________ **Date Goal Set:** ______________

Monthly progress toward the goal:

Update:

1st Day Of:		
1st Day Of:		
1st Day Of:		
1st Day Of:		
1st Day Of:		
1st Day Of:		
1st Day Of:		
1st Day Of:		
1st Day Of:		
1st Day Of:		
1st Day Of:		
1st Day Of:		

Date goal achieved:___________

☐ GOAL ACHIEVED

Scriptures I declare for this goal:

Seed I sow for this goal:

Goal: ______________________________ **Date Goal Set:** ____________

Monthly progress toward the goal:

Update:

1st Day Of:

1st Day Of:

1st Day Of:

1st Day Of:

1st Day Of:

1st Day Of:

1st Day Of:

1st Day Of:

1st Day Of:

1st Day Of:

1st Day Of:

1st Day Of:

Date goal achieved:__________

☐ GOAL ACHIEVED

Scriptures I declare for this goal:

Seed I sow for this goal:

Goal: ______________________________ **Date Goal Set:** ____________

Monthly progress toward the goal:

1st Day Of:

1st Day Of:

1st Day Of:

1st Day Of:

1st Day Of:

1st Day Of:

1st Day Of:

1st Day Of:

1st Day Of:

1st Day Of:

1st Day Of:

1st Day Of:

Update:

Date goal achieved:___________

☐ GOAL ACHIEVED

Scriptures I declare for this goal:

Seed I sow for this goal:

Goal: ______________________________ **Date Goal Set:** ____________

Monthly progress toward the goal:

Update:

1st Day Of:		
1st Day Of:		
1st Day Of:		
1st Day Of:		
1st Day Of:		
1st Day Of:		
1st Day Of:		
1st Day Of:		
1st Day Of:		
1st Day Of:		
1st Day Of:		
1st Day Of:		

Date goal achieved:__________

☐ GOAL ACHIEVED

Scriptures I declare for this goal:

Seed I sow for this goal:

Goal: ______________________________ **Date Goal Set:** ____________

Monthly progress toward the goal:

Update:

1st Day Of:		
1st Day Of:		
1st Day Of:		
1st Day Of:		
1st Day Of:		
1st Day Of:		
1st Day Of:		
1st Day Of:		
1st Day Of:		
1st Day Of:		
1st Day Of:		
1st Day Of:		

Date goal achieved:____________

☐ **GOAL ACHIEVED**

Scriptures I declare for this goal:

Seed I sow for this goal:

Goal: ______________________ **Date Goal Set:** __________

Monthly progress toward the goal: **Update:**

1st Day Of:		
1st Day Of:		
1st Day Of:		
1st Day Of:		
1st Day Of:		
1st Day Of:		
1st Day Of:		
1st Day Of:		
1st Day Of:		
1st Day Of:		
1st Day Of:		
1st Day Of:		

Date goal achieved:__________

☐ GOAL ACHIEVED

Scriptures I declare for this goal:

Seed I sow for this goal:

Goal: ______________________ **Date Goal Set:** ____________

Monthly progress toward the goal:

Update:

1st Day Of:

1st Day Of:

1st Day Of:

1st Day Of:

1st Day Of:

1st Day Of:

1st Day Of:

1st Day Of:

1st Day Of:

1st Day Of:

1st Day Of:

1st Day Of:

Date goal achieved:__________

☐ GOAL ACHIEVED

Scriptures I declare for this goal:

Seed I sow for this goal:

Goal: ______________________ **Date Goal Set:** ____________

Monthly progress toward the goal:

1st Day Of:	
1st Day Of:	
1st Day Of:	
1st Day Of:	
1st Day Of:	
1st Day Of:	
1st Day Of:	
1st Day Of:	
1st Day Of:	
1st Day Of:	
1st Day Of:	
1st Day Of:	

Update:

Date goal achieved:__________

☐ GOAL ACHIEVED

Scriptures I declare for this goal:

Seed I sow for this goal:

Goal: ______________________ **Date Goal Set:** ____________

Monthly progress toward the goal:

1st Day Of:
1st Day Of:
1st Day Of:
1st Day Of:
1st Day Of:
1st Day Of:
1st Day Of:
1st Day Of:
1st Day Of:
1st Day Of:
1st Day Of:
1st Day Of:

Update:

Date goal achieved:___________

☐ GOAL ACHIEVED

Scriptures I declare for this goal:

Seed I sow for this goal:

Goal: ______________________ Date Goal Set: ______________

Monthly progress toward the goal: **Update:**

1st Day Of:		
1st Day Of:		
1st Day Of:		
1st Day Of:		
1st Day Of:		
1st Day Of:		
1st Day Of:		
1st Day Of:		
1st Day Of:		
1st Day Of:		
1st Day Of:		
1st Day Of:		

Date goal achieved:___________

☐ GOAL ACHIEVED

Scriptures I declare for this goal:

Seed I sow for this goal:

Goal: ______________________________ **Date Goal Set:** ____________

Monthly progress toward the goal:

1st Day Of:	
1st Day Of:	
1st Day Of:	
1st Day Of:	
1st Day Of:	
1st Day Of:	
1st Day Of:	
1st Day Of:	
1st Day Of:	
1st Day Of:	
1st Day Of:	
1st Day Of:	

Update:

Date goal achieved:___________

☐ GOAL ACHIEVED

Scriptures I declare for this goal:

Seed I sow for this goal:

Goal: ______________________ **Date Goal Set:** ____________

Monthly progress toward the goal:

Update:

1st Day Of:		
1st Day Of:		
1st Day Of:		
1st Day Of:		
1st Day Of:		
1st Day Of:		
1st Day Of:		
1st Day Of:		
1st Day Of:		
1st Day Of:		
1st Day Of:		
1st Day Of:		

Date goal achieved:___________

☐ GOAL ACHIEVED

Scriptures I declare for this goal:

Seed I sow for this goal:

Goal: ______________________________ **Date Goal Set:** ____________

Monthly progress toward the goal: **Update:**

1st Day Of:

1st Day Of:

1st Day Of:

1st Day Of:

1st Day Of:

1st Day Of:

1st Day Of:

1st Day Of:

1st Day Of:

1st Day Of:

1st Day Of:

1st Day Of:

Date goal achieved:___________

☐ GOAL ACHIEVED

Scriptures I declare for this goal:

Seed I sow for this goal:

Goal: ______________________________ **Date Goal Set:** ____________

Monthly progress toward the goal:

Update:

1st Day Of:

1st Day Of:

1st Day Of:

1st Day Of:

1st Day Of:

1st Day Of:

1st Day Of:

1st Day Of:

1st Day Of:

1st Day Of:

1st Day Of:

1st Day Of:

Date goal achieved:___________

☐ GOAL ACHIEVED

Scriptures I declare for this goal:

Seed I sow for this goal:

Goal: ______________________ **Date Goal Set:** ____________

Monthly progress toward the goal:

1st Day Of:	
1st Day Of:	
1st Day Of:	
1st Day Of:	
1st Day Of:	
1st Day Of:	
1st Day Of:	
1st Day Of:	
1st Day Of:	
1st Day Of:	
1st Day Of:	
1st Day Of:	

Update:

Date goal achieved:__________

☐ GOAL ACHIEVED

Scriptures I declare for this goal:

Seed I sow for this goal:

Goal: ______________________________ **Date Goal Set:** ____________

Monthly progress toward the goal:

Update:

1st Day Of:		
1st Day Of:		
1st Day Of:		
1st Day Of:		
1st Day Of:		
1st Day Of:		
1st Day Of:		
1st Day Of:		
1st Day Of:		
1st Day Of:		
1st Day Of:		
1st Day Of:		

Date goal achieved:__________

☐ GOAL ACHIEVED

Scriptures I declare for this goal:

Seed I sow for this goal:

Goal: ______________________________ **Date Goal Set:** ____________

Monthly progress toward the goal:

Update:

1st Day Of:

1st Day Of:

1st Day Of:

1st Day Of:

1st Day Of:

1st Day Of:

1st Day Of:

1st Day Of:

1st Day Of:

1st Day Of:

1st Day Of:

1st Day Of:

Date goal achieved:__________

☐ GOAL ACHIEVED

Scriptures I declare for this goal:

Seed I sow for this goal:

Goal: ______________________ **Date Goal Set:** ____________

Monthly progress toward the goal:

Update:

1st Day Of:	
1st Day Of:	
1st Day Of:	
1st Day Of:	
1st Day Of:	
1st Day Of:	
1st Day Of:	
1st Day Of:	
1st Day Of:	
1st Day Of:	
1st Day Of:	
1st Day Of:	

Date goal achieved:__________

☐ GOAL ACHIEVED

Scriptures I declare for this goal:

Seed I sow for this goal:

Goal: ______________________ **Date Goal Set:** ____________

Monthly progress toward the goal:

1st Day Of:	
1st Day Of:	
1st Day Of:	
1st Day Of:	
1st Day Of:	
1st Day Of:	
1st Day Of:	
1st Day Of:	
1st Day Of:	
1st Day Of:	
1st Day Of:	
1st Day Of:	

Update:

Date goal achieved:__________

☐ GOAL ACHIEVED

Scriptures I declare for this goal:

Seed I sow for this goal:

Goal: ______________________________ **Date Goal Set:** ____________

Monthly progress toward the goal:

Update:

1st Day Of:		
1st Day Of:		
1st Day Of:		
1st Day Of:		
1st Day Of:		
1st Day Of:		
1st Day Of:		
1st Day Of:		
1st Day Of:		
1st Day Of:		
1st Day Of:		
1st Day Of:		

Date goal achieved:___________

☐ GOAL ACHIEVED

Scriptures I declare for this goal:

Seed I sow for this goal:

Goal: ______________________ **Date Goal Set:** __________

Monthly progress toward the goal:

Update:

1st Day Of:		
1st Day Of:		
1st Day Of:		
1st Day Of:		
1st Day Of:		
1st Day Of:		
1st Day Of:		
1st Day Of:		
1st Day Of:		
1st Day Of:		
1st Day Of:		
1st Day Of:		

Date goal achieved:___________

☐ GOAL ACHIEVED

Scriptures I declare for this goal:

Seed I sow for this goal:

Goal: ______________________ **Date Goal Set:** ____________

Monthly progress toward the goal:

Update:

1st Day Of:		
1st Day Of:		
1st Day Of:		
1st Day Of:		
1st Day Of:		
1st Day Of:		
1st Day Of:		
1st Day Of:		
1st Day Of:		
1st Day Of:		
1st Day Of:		
1st Day Of:		

Date goal achieved:__________

☐ GOAL ACHIEVED

Scriptures I declare for this goal:

Seed I sow for this goal:

Goal: ______________________ **Date Goal Set:** ______________

Monthly progress toward the goal:

1st Day Of:

1st Day Of:

1st Day Of:

1st Day Of:

1st Day Of:

1st Day Of:

1st Day Of:

1st Day Of:

1st Day Of:

1st Day Of:

1st Day Of:

1st Day Of:

Update:

Date goal achieved:__________

☐ **GOAL ACHIEVED**

Scriptures I declare for this goal:

Seed I sow for this goal:

Goal: ______________________________ **Date Goal Set:** ____________

Monthly progress toward the goal:

1st Day Of:	
1st Day Of:	
1st Day Of:	
1st Day Of:	
1st Day Of:	
1st Day Of:	
1st Day Of:	
1st Day Of:	
1st Day Of:	
1st Day Of:	
1st Day Of:	
1st Day Of:	

Update:

Date goal achieved:___________

☐ GOAL ACHIEVED

Scriptures I declare for this goal:

Seed I sow for this goal:

Goal: ______________________________ **Date Goal Set:** ______________

Monthly progress toward the goal:

Update:

1st Day Of:

1st Day Of:

1st Day Of:

1st Day Of:

1st Day Of:

1st Day Of:

1st Day Of:

1st Day Of:

1st Day Of:

1st Day Of:

1st Day Of:

1st Day Of:

Date goal achieved:__________

☐ GOAL ACHIEVED

Scriptures I declare for this goal:

____
____
____
____
____
____

Seed I sow for this goal:

Goal: ______________________ **Date Goal Set:** ____________

Monthly progress toward the goal:

		Update:
1st Day Of:		
1st Day Of:		
1st Day Of:		
1st Day Of:		
1st Day Of:		
1st Day Of:		
1st Day Of:		
1st Day Of:		
1st Day Of:		
1st Day Of:		
1st Day Of:		
1st Day Of:		

Date goal achieved:___________

☐ GOAL ACHIEVED

Scriptures I declare for this goal:

Seed I sow for this goal:

Goal: ____________________ **Date Goal Set:** ____________

Monthly progress toward the goal:

Update:

1st Day Of:		
1st Day Of:		
1st Day Of:		
1st Day Of:		
1st Day Of:		
1st Day Of:		
1st Day Of:		
1st Day Of:		
1st Day Of:		
1st Day Of:		
1st Day Of:		
1st Day Of:		

Date goal achieved:__________

☐ GOAL ACHIEVED

Scriptures I declare for this goal:

Seed I sow for this goal:

Goal: ______________________ **Date Goal Set:** __________

Monthly progress toward the goal: **Update:**

1st Day Of:		
1st Day Of:		
1st Day Of:		
1st Day Of:		
1st Day Of:		
1st Day Of:		
1st Day Of:		
1st Day Of:		
1st Day Of:		
1st Day Of:		
1st Day Of:		
1st Day Of:		

Date goal achieved:__________

GOAL ACHIEVED

Scriptures I declare for this goal:

Seed I sow for this goal:

Goal: ______________________ **Date Goal Set:** ____________

Monthly progress toward the goal:

Update:

1st Day Of:

1st Day Of:

1st Day Of:

1st Day Of:

1st Day Of:

1st Day Of:

1st Day Of:

1st Day Of:

1st Day Of:

1st Day Of:

1st Day Of:

1st Day Of:

Date goal achieved:__________

☐ GOAL ACHIEVED

Scriptures I declare for this goal:

Seed I sow for this goal:

Goal: ______________________ **Date Goal Set:** ____________

Monthly progress toward the goal:

Update:

1st Day Of:		
1st Day Of:		
1st Day Of:		
1st Day Of:		
1st Day Of:		
1st Day Of:		
1st Day Of:		
1st Day Of:		
1st Day Of:		
1st Day Of:		
1st Day Of:		
1st Day Of:		

Date goal achieved:__________

☐ GOAL ACHIEVED

Scriptures I declare for this goal:

Seed I sow for this goal:

Goal: ______________________ **Date Goal Set:** __________

Monthly progress toward the goal:

Update:

1st Day Of:		
1st Day Of:		
1st Day Of:		
1st Day Of:		
1st Day Of:		
1st Day Of:		
1st Day Of:		
1st Day Of:		
1st Day Of:		
1st Day Of:		
1st Day Of:		
1st Day Of:		

Date goal achieved:__________

☐ GOAL ACHIEVED

Scriptures I declare for this goal:

Seed I sow for this goal:

Goal: ______________________ **Date Goal Set:** ____________

Monthly progress toward the goal:

Update:

1st Day Of:

1st Day Of:

1st Day Of:

1st Day Of:

1st Day Of:

1st Day Of:

1st Day Of:

1st Day Of:

1st Day Of:

1st Day Of:

1st Day Of:

1st Day Of:

Date goal achieved:__________

☐ GOAL ACHIEVED

Scriptures I declare for this goal:

Seed I sow for this goal:

Goal: ______________________ **Date Goal Set:** ____________

Monthly progress toward the goal:

Update:

1st Day Of:		
1st Day Of:		
1st Day Of:		
1st Day Of:		
1st Day Of:		
1st Day Of:		
1st Day Of:		
1st Day Of:		
1st Day Of:		
1st Day Of:		
1st Day Of:		
1st Day Of:		

Date goal achieved:__________

☐ GOAL ACHIEVED

Scriptures I declare for this goal:

Seed I sow for this goal:

Goal: ______________________ **Date Goal Set:** ______________

Monthly progress toward the goal:

Monthly progress toward the goal		Update
1st Day Of:		
1st Day Of:		
1st Day Of:		
1st Day Of:		
1st Day Of:		
1st Day Of:		
1st Day Of:		
1st Day Of:		
1st Day Of:		
1st Day Of:		
1st Day Of:		
1st Day Of:		

Date goal achieved:__________

☐ GOAL ACHIEVED

Scriptures I declare for this goal:

Seed I sow for this goal:

Goal: ______________________________ **Date Goal Set:** ______________

Monthly progress toward the goal:

Update:

1st Day Of:		
1st Day Of:		
1st Day Of:		
1st Day Of:		
1st Day Of:		
1st Day Of:		
1st Day Of:		
1st Day Of:		
1st Day Of:		
1st Day Of:		
1st Day Of:		
1st Day Of:		

Date goal achieved:__________

☐ GOAL ACHIEVED

Scriptures I declare for this goal:

Seed I sow for this goal:

Goal: ______________________________ **Date Goal Set:** ____________

Monthly progress toward the goal:

Update:

1st Day Of:		
1st Day Of:		
1st Day Of:		
1st Day Of:		
1st Day Of:		
1st Day Of:		
1st Day Of:		
1st Day Of:		
1st Day Of:		
1st Day Of:		
1st Day Of:		
1st Day Of:		

Date goal achieved:___________

☐ GOAL ACHIEVED

Scriptures I declare for this goal:

Seed I sow for this goal:

Goal: ______________________________ **Date Goal Set:** ____________

Monthly progress toward the goal: **Update:**

1st Day Of:		
1st Day Of:		
1st Day Of:		
1st Day Of:		
1st Day Of:		
1st Day Of:		
1st Day Of:		
1st Day Of:		
1st Day Of:		
1st Day Of:		
1st Day Of:		
1st Day Of:		

Date goal achieved:__________

☐ GOAL ACHIEVED

Scriptures I declare for this goal:

Seed I sow for this goal:

Goal: ______________________ **Date Goal Set:** __________

Monthly progress toward the goal:

Update:

1st Day Of:		
1st Day Of:		
1st Day Of:		
1st Day Of:		
1st Day Of:		
1st Day Of:		
1st Day Of:		
1st Day Of:		
1st Day Of:		
1st Day Of:		
1st Day Of:		
1st Day Of:		

Date goal achieved:__________

☐ GOAL ACHIEVED

Scriptures I declare for this goal:

Seed I sow for this goal:

Goal: ______________________ Date Goal Set: ____________

Monthly progress toward the goal:

1st Day Of:	
1st Day Of:	
1st Day Of:	
1st Day Of:	
1st Day Of:	
1st Day Of:	
1st Day Of:	
1st Day Of:	
1st Day Of:	
1st Day Of:	
1st Day Of:	
1st Day Of:	

Update:

Date goal achieved:__________

☐ GOAL ACHIEVED

Scriptures I declare for this goal:

Seed I sow for this goal:

Goal: ______________________ **Date Goal Set:** ______________

Monthly progress toward the goal: **Update:**

1st Day Of:		
1st Day Of:		
1st Day Of:		
1st Day Of:		
1st Day Of:		
1st Day Of:		
1st Day Of:		
1st Day Of:		
1st Day Of:		
1st Day Of:		
1st Day Of:		
1st Day Of:		

Date goal achieved:___________

☐ GOAL ACHIEVED

Scriptures I declare for this goal:

Seed I sow for this goal:

Goal: ______________________ **Date Goal Set:** ______________

Monthly progress toward the goal: **Update:**

1st Day Of:		
1st Day Of:		
1st Day Of:		
1st Day Of:		
1st Day Of:		
1st Day Of:		
1st Day Of:		
1st Day Of:		
1st Day Of:		
1st Day Of:		
1st Day Of:		
1st Day Of:		

Date goal achieved:__________

☐ GOAL ACHIEVED

Scriptures I declare for this goal:

Seed I sow for this goal:

Goal: ______________________________ **Date Goal Set:** ____________

Monthly progress toward the goal:

Update:

Monthly progress toward the goal:		Update:
1st Day Of:		
1st Day Of:		
1st Day Of:		
1st Day Of:		
1st Day Of:		
1st Day Of:		
1st Day Of:		
1st Day Of:		
1st Day Of:		
1st Day Of:		
1st Day Of:		
1st Day Of:		

Date goal achieved:__________

☐ GOAL ACHIEVED

Scriptures I declare for this goal:

Seed I sow for this goal:

5

years from now

It's exactly 5 years from today.

What is the year? How old are you? What does your life look like? If you're married, how long will you have been married by then? If you have children, what are their ages 5 years from now? Where do you live? Where do you work? What is your salary? How much money have you saved? Where have you traveled? What impact have you made? What have you done in the past 5 years?

Go through your current routine each morning, afternoon and evening. It's exactly the same 5 years from now. Are you content with that? Are you satisfied? Are you bored? Are you disappointed? Are you miserable? Do you feel that you missed out on something you should have done? What is it?

What would make you feel satisfied, confident and pleased with yourself if you pursue "this thing" 5 years from now? Then, do it. Live your life on purpose. Take the time to go in another room quietly, by yourself and THINK.

The next 5 years of your life can be the most productive, most exciting and most rewarding years of your life...or just another 5 years. You can achieve more of your dreams over these next 5 years than the previous 15-20 combined. It's entirely up to you and your ability to imagine, to dream, to plan, to act.

Don't be one of those people who come to the end of their life and say, "I wish I would have" or "I always wanted to." Whatever it is, do it. Think it. Write it. Pursue it.

This notebook is designed to stretch your imagination and wake up the dreamer in you. If you always wanted to take up flying lessons, in the next 5 years, you could be a pilot. If you always wanted to learn a foreign language, in the next 5 years, you could be fluent. If you always wanted to be a teacher, but you got married young and had kids...in the next 5 years, you could be teaching!

Decide what you want to do and where you want to end up. Give yourself permission to dream.

BAMBOO TREE

The 1st year: you plant the seed, water it and fertilize it . . . nothing happens.

The 2nd year: you water it and fertilize it . . . nothing.

The 3rd year: you water it and fertilize it . . . nothing.

The 4th year: you water it and fertilize it . . . nothing.

The 5th year: it grows as much as 80 feet!

All those years when it appeared nothing was happening, the Chinese Bamboo tree was developing a massive root system in order to support the growth it would have in its 5th year.

I'M POSSIBLE... NOT IMPOSSIBLE

What are those impossibilities deep down in your spirit that have lay dormant for far too long? What if you were to give this spiral notebook to your grandchildren? Would they be inspired by your life, by your ability to dream and pursue those dreams? Or would they find empty pages communicating a clear message of nothing?

It's time to expose yourself to the opportunities that God has for you. Give yourself permission to dream. Stop thinking it could never happen to you. Why not you? Why not now? One dream can launch the journey of a lifetime.

"See it. Say it. Seize it." - Jerry Savelle

It's important for you to see what it is that you're pursuing. Get pictures off the internet, use postcards, clip out magazine pages and place them in this notebook.

As you keep your dreams before you, passion will stay fueled and ideas will be birthed. Remember this: the vision comes first, the ideas come second.

DOES YOUR AGE MATTER?

At 11 months Brooke Shields is hired for her first television commercial as the Ivory Snow baby.

At 4 Shirley Temple began her film career and three years later, received an Academy Award.

At 8 Mozart composes his first symphony.

At 11 Michael Jackson sings the smash hit "ABC" with the Jackson Five.

At 12 Pocahontas saves the life of Captain John Smith.

At 13 Anne Frank begins writing in her diary (that would go around the world) before she and her family are forced into hiding from the Nazis.

At 15 Justin Bieber became the first artist to have seven songs from a debut album chart the Billboard Hot 100 list.

At 18 Cassius Clay (later Muhammad Ali) wins the light heavyweight boxing gold medal at the 1960 Olympic Games.

At 18 Tommy Hilfiger opens his first clothing store.

At 20 Debbi Fields founded Mrs. Fields cookie company.

At 38 Terri Savelle Foy launched her ministry and terri.com.

At 42 Joyce Meyer launched her worldwide ministry in Fenton, MO.

At 45 Susan Sarandon wins the first of three Academy Award Best Actress nominations and gives birth to her third child.

At 45 Henry Ford introduces the automobile called Model T.

At 49 Julia Childs writes Mastering the Art of French Cooking.

At 52 Leonardo da Vinci completes the Mona Lisa.

At 52 Ray Kroc starts a fast food chain called McDonalds.

At 56 Gustave Eiffel completes the design for the Paris tower.

At 58 Bruce Springsteen & the E Street Band named Best Live Band of the Year in 2008 by Rolling Stone magazine.

At 64 Betty Ford opens her first clinic to treat substance abuse.

At 65 Colonel Sanders founds Kentucky Fried Chicken.

At 71 Coco Chanel debuts the designer Chanel suit.

At 72 Michel Angelo designs St Peter's Basilica in Rome.

At 73 Ronald Reagan is re-elected as President of the United States of America.

At 76 Henry Fonda wins his first Oscar (after 46 years of acting) for his role in On Golden Pond.

At 79 Ben Franklin invents bifocal eyeglasses

At 83 Winston Churchill completes "A History of the English – Speaking Peoples"

At 90 Nelson Mandela adorns the cover of Time Magazine

At 97 Wisconsin man Simon Stern divorces his wife, Ida

At 98 In Athens, Greece, Dimitrion Yordanidis runs a marathon in 7 hours 33 minutes

At 99 Abraham's wife, Sarah, gave birth to their son, Isaac.

At 100 Ichijirou Araya climbs Mt. Fuji

"One isn't necessarily born with courage, but one is born with potential."

“THINKING IS THE
HARDEST WORK
THERE IS—WHICH IS
PROBABLY THE REASON
SO FEW ENGAGE IN IT.”

- HENRY FORD

MY DREAMS & GOALS

TERRI SAVELLE FOY

August 22, 2006

I wrote what I saw in my imagination.
I visualized:

1. TV. I see myself teaching on a weekly Christian broadcast with my dad.
2. Books. I see myself writing books that will be sold in bookstores across the USA.
3. Women's Conferences. I see myself hosting creative conferences "with a theme" for women and teenage girls.
4. Helping Troubled Teenage Girls. I see myself teaching young girls and/or providing resources to help them make their dreams bigger than their memories.
5. France. I see myself speaking in churches and conferences all over France.

5 years later: August 22, 2011 (I updated my 5 year plan)

1. TV. I am currently co-hosting a weekly Christian TV show with my dad.
2. Books. My 1st hardback book launched in 2010 and is sold in major bookstores across the US including Amazon and the ebook format.
3. Women's Conferences. I launched a women's event in 2010 called "Icing" that is teaching ladies to pursue their dreams.
4. Helping Troubled Teenage Girls. I invest my resources (books, CDs, dream journals) in girls' homes across the globe; as well as teach in the homes.
5. France. I am speaking in venues across the nation of France each year as well as distributing my books in French (which can be purchased in bookstores in Paris).

Everything I wrote happened.

YOU

5 YEARS FROM NOW

DATE ___________________

AGE ____________________

MY LIFE AND WHAT I'VE ACCOMPLISHED

Use the following pages to post pictures of places you will have gone, things you will have accomplished, money you will have saved and given, experiences you will have had, and items you will own 5 years from now.

Goal: ______________________ **Date Goal Set:** ______________

Progress toward the goal:

Year 1	
Year 2	
Year 3	
Year 4	
Year 5	

Update:

Date goal achieved:__________

☐ GOAL ACHIEVED

Scriptures I declare for this goal:

Seed I sow for this goal:

Goal: ______________________ **Date Goal Set:** __________

Progress toward the goal:

Update:

	Progress toward the goal	Update
Year 1		
Year 2		
Year 3		
Year 4		
Year 5		

Date goal achieved:___________

☐ GOAL ACHIEVED

Scriptures I declare for this goal:

Seed I sow for this goal:

Goal: ______________________________ **Date Goal Set:** ____________

Progress toward the goal:

Update:

	Progress toward the goal	Update
Year 1		
Year 2		
Year 3		
Year 4		
Year 5		

Date goal achieved:__________

☐ GOAL ACHIEVED

Scriptures I declare for this goal:

Seed I sow for this goal:

Goal: ______________________________ **Date Goal Set:** ____________

Progress toward the goal:

Update:

	Progress toward the goal	Update
Year 1		
Year 2		
Year 3		
Year 4		
Year 5		

Date goal achieved:___________

☐ GOAL ACHIEVED

Scriptures I declare for this goal:

Seed I sow for this goal:

Goal: ______________________ Date Goal Set: ______________

Progress toward the goal:

Year 1	
Year 2	
Year 3	
Year 4	
Year 5	

Update:

Date goal achieved:___________

☐ GOAL ACHIEVED

Scriptures I declare for this goal:

Seed I sow for this goal:

Goal: ______________________ **Date Goal Set:** ____________

Progress toward the goal: **Update:**

Year 1		
Year 2		
Year 3		
Year 4		
Year 5		